Alfie sat down. He felt sad. He was hot. He needed to shelter from the sun.

1

Alfie saw some trees and bushes in the distance. He went towards them. Some monkeys came from the trees to meet him.

'Have you seen the elephants?' asked Alfie. 'They have gone away. I am all by myself.'

The monkeys had not seen the elephants. 'Come with us,' they said. 'Come and shelter under the trees.'

4

The monkeys took Alfie to the trees. He flopped down on the ground. The monkeys gave him leaves and twigs to eat.

They chatted to him to cheer him up. 'We will help you find the elephants,' they said.

Suddenly there was a loud grumbling noise. The monkeys rushed up into the trees. Alfie was all by himself on the ground.

The monkeys had gone, but Alfie was not by himself. A very large rhinoceros was in front of him.